PENGUIN MODERN CL

The World of Sex

Henry Valentine Mille
ca's most controversial and influential writers. Born in New York City to Lutheran German parents, Miller grew up in Brooklyn. Throughout the 1910s and early 1920s, he drove cabs, worked in his father's tailoring shop, and eventually became a messenger for the Western Union Telegraph Company. While working there he wrote his first novels, *Moloch* and *Crazy Cock* (1927–1928). He considered them unsatisfying, and both remained unpublished until after his death.

In 1928 Miller travelled to Paris with his second wife, musical-hall dancer June Mansfield, and in 1930, at the age of 39, he moved to Paris on his own. There he met Anaïs Nin, who became his lover, and started working on *Tropic of Cancer*. Published in 1934 by the Obelisk Press in Paris, the novel was quickly banned in the US and the UK on the grounds of obscenity – the dust jacket came wrapped with a warning: 'Not to be imported into the United States or Great Britain'. Most of his subsequent books, including *Tropic of Capricorn* (1939), had to be smuggled into America until 1964, when the US Supreme Court ruled that they were literary works rather than pornography.

In 1939 Miller went to Greece to visit Lawrence Durrell; his sojourn there inspired *The Colossus of Maroussi*. Cut off by the war and forced to return to America in 1940, Miller, adrift in his native country, published *The Air-Conditioned Nightmare* (1941). He finally settled for good in California, where he wrote the Rosy Crucifixion trilogy: *Sexus* (1949), *Nexus* (1953) and *Plexus* (1959). Alongside his novels, he published literary criticism, travel memoirs and portraits of artists, and was himself a skilled watercolourist.

HENRY MILLER

The World of Sex

PENGUIN BOOKS

PENGUIN CLASSICS

UK | USA | Canada | Ireland | Australia
India | New Zealand | South Africa

Penguin Books is part of the Penguin Random House group of companies whose addresses can be found at global.penguinrandomhouse.com.

First published privately in the United States of America 1940
Published in Penguin Classics 2015
001

Set in 11.25/13.75 pt Dante MT Std
Typeset by Jouve (UK), Milton Keynes
Printed in Great Britain by Clays Ltd, St Ives plc

A CIP catalogue record for this book is available from the British Library

ISBN: 978–0–141–39915–7

www.greenpenguin.co.uk

Contents

Preface 1

The World of Sex 3

Notes 85
Miller's Corrections to the Original Text 87

Note on the Text

The text in this edition is taken from the 'complete' Paris edition published in 1957 by Olympia Press, which was reproduced by Grove Press in 1959. The spelling and punctuation have been standardized, modernized and made consistent throughout.

Preface

The original version of this book was privately published by a man now dead. How many copies were made and sold I was never able to learn. The book was circulated under the counter and no records were kept of its sale. At least, I never received any.

With the death of the publisher the book has gone out of print. As it was never widely known, and since no publisher in England or America was likely to reprint it, I decided to have a new edition made in France, where all the banned books bearing my signature have been published, and still are.

However, before entrusting it to the mail, I thought it wise to reread what I had written so long ago. As I read, I began (quite involuntarily) making changes and corrections, never dreaming what I was letting myself in for. If the reader will turn to the reproductions in this volume, he will see for himself with what almost diabolical enthusiasm I plunged into this work of revision.*

Halfway along, it occurred to me that it might be of interest to readers, particularly those who are curious about an author's lucubrations, to put the two versions side by side.

I should add, since there is an apparent discrepancy between the new and the corrected pages, that I made another complete revision which is not shown here but from which this new printed version derives. The effort involved in making the second revision was greater but even more exciting than that connected with the first attempt.

I should also add that the primary purpose in altering the original text was not to change the thought but to clarify it. I hope that I have not failed.

– Henry Miller

The World of Sex

The bulk of my readers, I have often observed, fall into two distinct groups: in the one group those who claim to be repelled or disgusted by the liberal dosage of sex, and in the other those who are delighted to find that this element forms such a large ingredient. The first group numbers many who find the studies and essays not only commendable but superbly to their taste, and therefore are hard put to it to explain how one and the same individual could produce such vastly dissimilar works. In the second group there are those who profess to be annoyed with what they call my serious side and who consequently derive pleasure in denouncing all evidence of it as rot, piffle and mysticism. Only a few discerning souls seem capable of reconciling the supposedly contradictory aspects of a being who has endeavoured to withhold no part of himself in his written work.

On the other hand I find that, no matter how

violently disagreeable a reader's reaction may be to the written work, when we meet face to face he usually ends by accepting me wholeheartedly. From the many encounters I have had with my readers it would seem that antipathies are quickly dispelled in the living presence of an author. Repeated experiences of this sort have finally led me to believe that when I am able to make the written word convey the full essence of truth and sincerity, there will cease to exist any discrepancy between the man and the writer, between what I am and what I do or say. This, in my humble opinion, is the highest goal an author can set himself. The same aim – unification – is implicit in all religious striving. Perhaps, without knowing it, I have always been a religious person.

As to whether the sexual and the religious are conflicting and opposed, I would answer thus: every element or aspect of life, however necessitated, however questionable (to us), is susceptible to conversion, and indeed must be converted to other levels, in accordance with our growth and understanding. The effort to eliminate the 'repulsive' aspects of existence, which is the obsession of moralists, is not only absurd, but futile. One may succeed in repressing ugly, 'sinful' thoughts and desires, impulses and urges, but the results are patently disastrous. (Between being a saint and being a criminal there is little to choose.) To live out one's desires and, in so doing, subtly alter their nature is the aim of every individual who aspires to evolve. But desire is paramount and ineradicable, even when, as Buddhists express it, it passes over into its opposite. To free oneself from desire one has to *desire* to do so.

The subject is one which has always interested me profoundly. In youth, and long after, I was the victim of impulsive urges that were wholly beyond control. Of late, following upon a prolonged period of intense creative activity, I have become more than ever mystified by the morass of thoughts in which the perennial treatment of the subject is mired.

It was in 1935 that the book *Seraphita* was thrust into my hands by a friend who was an occultist. *Seraphita* remains today one of the high peaks of my explorations in the realm of thought. It is more than a book; it is an experience which the author perpetuated in words. From this work I passed to a study of that other memorable work of Balzac, *Louis Lambert*, then to an examination of Balzac's life. The results of these studies crystallized in the form of a treatise called 'Balzac and his Double'.* In writing it the conflict which had tormented me was resolved.

Few realize how ardently Balzac wrestled with the problem of the angel in man. I say this in order to confess that, in slightly different guise, this same problem has been an obsession with me my whole life long. In a sense I believe it has always been the chief preoccupation of every creative individual, almost exclusively his. Admittedly or not, the artist is obsessed with the thought of recreating the world in order to restore man's innocence. He knows, moreover, that man can only recover his innocence by regaining his freedom; freedom here meaning the death of the automaton.

In one of his essays, D. H. Lawrence pointed out that there were two great modes of life, the religious and the sexual. The former, he declared, took precedence over the latter. The sexual was the lesser way, he said. I have always thought that there is only one way, the way of truth, leading not to salvation but to enlightenment. However one civilization may differ from another, however the laws, customs, beliefs and worships of man may vary from one period to another, from one type or race of man to another, I perceive in the behaviour of the great spiritual leaders a singular concordance, an exemplification of truth and wholeness which even a child can grasp.

Does it seem out of character for the author of *Tropic of Cancer* to voice such views? Not if one probes beneath the surface! Liberally larded with the sexual as was that work, the concern of its author was not with sex, nor with religion, but with the problem of self-liberation. In *Tropic of Capricorn* the use of the obscene is more studied and deliberate, perhaps because of a heightened awareness of the exacting demands of the medium. The interlude called 'The Land of Fuck' is for me a high water mark in the fusion of symbol, myth and metaphor. Employed as a breakwater, it serves a double purpose. (Just as the clown acts in the circus not only relieve the tension but prepare one for still greater tension.) Though in the act of writing* there was only a dim realization of its meaning, with respect to its purpose there was absolute certitude. It was an achievement tantamount to jumping out of one's skin. In years to come this 'extravaganza' may offer an unsuspected clue to the nature of the author's inmost struggle. There is no need to disguise the fact that the crux of the conflict pertains to the rarely understood phenomenon of polarity. Between word and response there exists today only the feeblest flicker of a current. To attribute the dilemma, as do most thinkers, to social, political and economic disturbance is to confound the issue.

The real reason lies deeper. A new world is in the making, a new type of man is in the bud. The masses, destined now to suffer more cruelly than ever before, are paralyzed with dread and apprehension. They have withdrawn, like the shell-shocked, into their self-created tombs; they have lost all contact with reality except where their bodily needs are concerned. The body, of course, has long ceased to be the temple of the spirit. It is thus that man dies to the world – and to the Creator. In the course of disintegration, a process which may go on for centuries, life loses all significance. An unearthly activity, manifested with equal ferocity in the pursuits of scholars, thinkers, men of science as in the doings of militarists, politicians and plunderers, screens the ever waning presence of the living flame. This abnormal activity is itself the sign of approaching death.

Of all this I knew or understood very little when first I took up the pen. Before I could make a proper start I had to go through my 'little death'. The false start, which lasted ten years, enabled me to die to the world. In Paris, as everyone now knows, I found myself.

In that first year or two, in Paris, I was literally annihilated. There was nothing left of the writer I had hoped to be, only the writer I had to be. (In finding my way I found my voice.) The *Tropic of Cancer* is a blood-soaked testament revealing the ravages of my struggle in the womb of death. The strong odour of sex which it purveys is really the aroma of birth; it is disagreeable or repulsive only to those who fail to recognize its significance.

The *Tropic of Capricorn* represents the transition to a more knowing phase: from consciousness of self to consciousness of purpose. Henceforward, what metamorphoses occur manifest even more through conduct than through the written word. The beginning of a conflict between the writer who is resolved to finish his task and the man who knows deep down that the desire to express oneself must never be limited to a single medium – to art, let us say – but to every phase of life. A battle, more or less conscious, between duty and desire. That part of a man which belongs to the world seeking to do its duty; the part which belongs to God striving to fulfil the demands of destiny, which are unstateable. The difficulty: to adapt to that desolate plane where only one's own powers will sustain one. From this point on, the problem is to write retrospectively and act forwardly. To slip is to sink into an abyss from which there is no rescue possible. The struggle is on all fronts, and it is ceaseless and remorseless.

Like every man, I am my own worst enemy. Unlike most men, however, I also know that I am my own saviour. I know that freedom means responsibility. I know too how easily desire may be converted to deed. Even when I close my eyes I must be careful how I dream and of what, for now only the thinnest veil separates dream from reality.

How large or small a part sex plays in one's life seems relatively unimportant. Some of the greatest achievements we know of have been accomplished by individuals who had little or no sex life. On the other hand, we know from the lives of certain artists – men of the first rank – that their imposing works would never have been produced had they not been immersed in sex. In the case of a certain few these periods of exceptional creativity coincided with extravagant sexual indulgence. Neither abstinence nor indulgence explains anything. In the realm of sex, as in other realms, we speak of a norm – but the normal accounts for nothing more than what is true, statistically, for the great mass of men and women. What may be normal, sane, healthful for the vast majority affords us no criterion of behaviour where the exceptional individual is concerned. The man of genius, whether through his work or by personal example, seems ever to be blazing the truth that each one is a law unto himself, and that the way to fulfilment is through recognition and realization of the fact that we are each and all unique.

Our laws and customs relate to social life, our life in common, which is the lesser side of existence. Real life begins when we are alone, face to face with our unknown self. What happens when we come together is determined by our inner soliloquies. The crucial and truly pivotal events which mark our way are the fruits of silence and of solitude. We attribute much to chance meetings, refer to them as turning points in our life, but these encounters could never have occurred had we not made ourselves ready for them. If we possessed more awareness, these fortuitous encounters would yield still greater rewards. It is only at certain unpredictable times that we are fully attuned, fully expectant, and thus in a position to receive the favours of fortune. The man who is thoroughly awake knows that every 'happening' is packed with significance. He knows that not only is his own life being altered but that eventually the entire world must be affected.

The part which sex plays in a man's life varies greatly with the individual, as we know. It is not impossible that there may be a pattern which includes the widest variations. When I think of sex I think of it as a domain only partially explored; the greater part, for me at least, remains mysterious and unknown, possibly for ever unknowable. The same holds for other aspects of the life force. We may know a little or much, but the further we push the more the horizon recedes. We are enveloped in a sea of forces which seem to defy our puny intelligence. Until we accept the fact that life itself is founded in mystery we shall learn nothing.

Sex, then, like everything else, is largely a mystery. That is what I am trying to say. I do not pretend to be a great explorer in this realm. My own adventures are as nothing compared to those of the ordinary Don Juan. For a man of the big cities I think my exploits are modest and altogether normal. As an artist, my adventures seem in no way singular or remarkable. My explorations have, however, enabled me to make a few discoveries which may one day bear fruit. Let us put it this way – that I have charted certain islands which may serve as stepping stones when the great routes are opened up.

There was a period in Paris, just after I had undergone a conversion, when I was able to visualize with hallucinating clarity the whole pattern of my past. I seemed possessed with the power to recall anything and everything I chose to recall; even without wishing it, the events and encounters which had happened long ago crowded upon my consciousness with such force, such vividness, as to be almost unbearable. Everything that had happened to me acquired significance, that is what I remember most about this experience. Every meeting or chance encounter proved to be an event; every relationship fell into its true place. Suddenly I felt able to look back upon the truly vast horde of men, women and children I had known – animals too – and see the thing as a whole, see it as clearly and prophetically as one sees the constellations on a clear winter's night. I could detect the orbits which my planetary friends and acquaintances had described, and I could also detect amidst these dizzying movements the erratic course which I myself had traced – as nebula, sun, moon, satellite, meteor, comet . . . and stardust. I observed the periods of opposition and conjunction as well as the periods of partial or total eclipse. I saw that there was a deep and lasting connection between myself and all the other human beings with whom it had been my lot – and my privilege! – to come in contact at one time or another. What is still more important is that I saw within the frame of the actual the potential being which I am. In these lucid moments I saw myself as one of the most solitary and at the same time one of the most companionable of men. It was as though, for a brief interval, the curtain had dropped, the struggle halted. In the great amphitheatre which I had supposed to be empty and meaningless, there unfolded before my eyes the tumultuous creation, of which I was, fortunately and at long last, a part.

I said men, women and children . . . They were all there; all equally important. I might have added – books, mountains, rivers, lakes, cities, forests, creatures of the air and creatures of the deep. Names, places, people, events, ideas, dreams, reveries, wishes, hopes, plans and frustrations – all, when summoned, were as vivid and alive as they had ever been. Everything fell into latitude and longitude, so to speak. There were great tracts of fog, which was metaphysics; broad, flaming belts, the religions; burning comets, whose tails spelt hope. And so on . . . And there was sex. But what *was* sex? Like the deity, it was omnipresent. It pervaded everything. Perhaps the whole universe of the past, to give an image for it, was none other than a mythological monster from which the world, my world, had been whelped, but which failed to disappear with the act of creation, remaining below, supporting the world (and its own self) upon its back.

For me this singular experience now occupies a place in my memory akin to that of the Flood in the depths of man's unconscious. The day the waters receded the mountain stood revealed. There was I, stranded on the topmost peak, in the ark which I had built at the command of a mysterious voice. Suddenly the doves flew forth, shattering the mists with their flaming plumage . . . All this, unbelievable if you like, followed upon a catastrophe now so deeply buried as to be unrememberable.

That mythological monster! Let me add a few recollections before it loses form and substance . . .

To begin with, it was as though I had come out of a deep trance. And, like that figure of old, I found myself in the belly of a whale. The colour which bathed my retina was a warm grey. Everything I touched felt delicious, as with the surgeon when he delves into our warm innards. The climate was temperate, tending towards warmth rather than coolth. In short, a typical uterine atmosphere replete with all the Babylonian comforts of the effete. Born over-civilized, I felt thoroughly at ease. All was familiar and pleasurable to my over-refined sensorium. I could count with certitude on my black coffee, my liqueur, my Havana-Havana, my silk dressing gown, and all the other necessities of the man of leisure. No grim struggle for existence, no bread and butter problems, no social or psychological complexes to iron out. I was an emancipated ne'er-do-well from the start. When there was nothing better to do I would send out for the evening paper and, after a glance at the headlines, I would sedulously devour the ads, the social gossip, the theatre notices, and so on, down through the obituary *récit*.*

For some strange reason I displayed an abnormal interest in the fauna and flora of this uterine domain, I looked about me with the cool, witless glance of the scientist. ('The daffy herbotomist', I dubbed myself.) Within these labyrinthian folds I discovered innumerable marvels . . . And now I must break off – since all this has served only as a reminder – to speak of the first little cunt I ever examined.

I was about five or six at the time, and the incident

took place in a cellar. The after-image, which solidified at the appropriate time in the form of an incongruity, I labelled 'the man in the iron mask'. Just a few years ago, in riffling the pages of a book containing reproductions of primitive masks, I stumbled upon a womb-like mask which, when one lifted the flap, revealed the head of a full-grown man. Perhaps the shock of seeing this full-blown head peering from the womb was the first genuine response I had had to the question which voiced itself that instant long ago when I had my first serious look at a vagina. (In the *Tropic of Cancer*, it may be remembered, I portrayed a companion who had never recovered from this obsession. He is still, I believe, prying open one cunt after another in order, as he puts it to himself, to get at the mystery it holds.)

It was a hairless world I gazed upon. The very absence of hair, so I now think, served to stimulate the imagination, helped populate the arid region which surrounded the place of mystery. We were concerned less with what lay within than with the future vegetal decor which we imagined would one day beautify this strange wasteland. Depending on the time of the year, the age of the players, the place,. as well as other more complicated factors, the genitals of certain little creatures seemed as variegated, when I think of it now, as the strange entities which people the imaginative minds of occultists. What presented itself to our impressionable minds was a nameless phantasmagoria swarming with images which were real, tangible, thinkable, yet nameless, for they were unconnected with the world of experience wherein everything has a name, a place and a date. Thus it was that certain little girls were referred to as possessing (hidden beneath their skirts) such queer effects as magnolias, cologne bottles, velvet buttons, rubber mice . . . God only knows what. That every little girl had a crack was of course common knowledge. Now and then rumour had it that such and such a one had no crack at all; of another it might be said that she was a 'morphodite'. Morphodite was a strange and frightening term which no one could clearly define. Sometimes it implied the notion of double sex, sometimes other things, to wit, that where the crack ought to be there was a cloven hoof or a row of warts. *Better not ask to see it!* – that was the dominant thought.

A curious thing about this period was the conviction which obtained among us that some of our little playmates were definitely bad, i.e. incipient whores or sluts. Some girls already possessed a vile vocabulary pertaining to this mysterious realm. Some would do forbidden things if given a little gift or a few coppers. There were others, I must add, who were looked upon as angels, nothing less. They were that angelic, in fact, that none of us ever thought of them as owning a crack. These angelic creatures didn't even pee.

I make mention of these early attempts at characterization, because later in life, having witnessed the development of some of the 'loose ones', I was impressed by the accuracy of our observations. Occasionally one of the angels also fell into the gutter, and remained there. Usually, however, they met a different fate. Some led an unhappy life, either through marrying the wrong man or not marrying at all, some were stricken with mysterious illnesses, others were crucified by their parents. Many whom we had dubbed sluts turned out to be excellent human beings, jolly, flexible, generous, human to the core, though often a bit the worse for wear.

With adolescence another kind of curiosity developed – namely, the desire to find out how 'the thing' functioned. Girls of ten or twelve were often induced to adopt the most grotesque poses in order to demonstrate how they made pee-pee. The skilled ones were reputed to be able to lie on the floor and piss up to the ceiling. Some were already being accused of using candles – or broomsticks. The conversation, when it got round to this topic, became rather thick and complicated; it was tinged with a flavour strangely reminiscent of the atmosphere which invested the early

Greek schools of philosophy – logic, I mean, played a greater role than empiricism. The desire to explore with the naked eye was subordinated to a greater urge, one which I now realize was none other than the need to talk it out, to discuss the subject ad nauseam. The intellect, alas, had already begun to exact its tribute. How 'the thing' functioned was smothered by the deeper query – *why?* With the birth of the questioning faculty, sorrow set in. Our world, hitherto so natural, so marvellous, slipped its moorings. Henceforth, nothing was absolutely so any more: everything could be proved – and disproved. The hair which now began to sprout on the sacred Mons Venus was repellent. Even the little angels were breaking out in pimples. And there were some who were bleeding between the legs.

Masturbation was far more interesting. In bed, or in the warm bath, one could imagine himself lying with the Queen of Sheba, or with a burlesque queen whose tantalizing body, featured everywhere, infected one's every thought. One wondered what these women pictured with skirts whirling above their heads did when they appeared before the footlights. Some said that they brazenly removed every stitch of their gorgeous costumes and stood holding their boobies invitingly – until the sailors made a stampede for the stage. Often, so it was said, the curtain had to be rung down and the police summoned.

Something was wrong with the girls we used to play with. They weren't the same any more. In fact, everything was changing, and for the worse. As for the boys, they were being farmed out one after another. Schooling was a luxury reserved for the children of the rich. Out there, 'in the world', from all reports, it was nothing but a slave market. Yes, the world *was* crumbling about us. *Our* world.

And then there were places known as penitentiaries, reformatories, homes for wayward girls, insane asylums and so on.

Before things were to go utterly to smash, however, a wonderful event might occur. A party, no less. Where someone very precious, someone hardly more than a name, was certain to make an appearance.

To me these 'events' now seem like those fabulous balls which precede a revolution. One looked forward to being violently happy, happier than one had ever been before, yet one also had the presentiment that some untoward thing would happen, something which would affect one's whole life. A deal of sly whispering always surrounded the coming event. It went on among parents, older brothers and sisters, and among the neighbours. Everyone seemed to know more about one's sacred emotional life than was warranted. The whole neighbourhood suddenly seemed abnormally interested in one's slightest doings. One was watched, spied upon, talked about behind one's back. Such great emphasis was put on age. The way people said, 'He's fifteen now!' entrained the most embarrassing implications. It all seemed like a sinister puppet show which the elders were staging, a spectacle in which we would be the ridiculous performers there to be laughed at, mocked, goaded to say and do unaccountable things.

After weeks of anxiety the day would finally arrive. The girl too, at the last moment. Just when everything augured well, when all it needed – for what? – was a word, a look, a gesture, one discovered to his dismay that he had grown dumb, that his feet were rooted to the spot on which they had been planted ever since entering the place. Maybe once during the whole long evening did the precious one offer the slightest token of recognition. To move close to her, to brush her skirt, inhale the fragrance of her breath, what a difficult, what a monumental feat! The others appeared to move at will, freely. All that he and she seemed capable of was to slowly gravitate about such uninteresting objects as the piano, the umbrella stand, the bookcase. Only by accident did they seem destined now and then to converge upon one another. Even so, even when all the mysterious, supercharged forces in the room seemed to be pushing them towards each other, something always intervened to make them drift apart. To make it worse, the parents behaved in the most unfeeling fashion, pushing and jostling couples about, gesticulating like goats, making rude remarks, asking pointed questions. In short, acting like idiots.

The evening would come to an end with a great handshaking all around. Some kissed each other good-bye. The bold ones! Those who lacked the courage to behave with such abandon, those who cared, who felt deeply, in other words, were lost in the shuffle. No one noticed their discomfiture. They were non-existent.

Time to go. The streets are empty. He starts walking homewards. Not the slightest trace of fatigue. Elated, though nothing had really happened. Indeed, it had been an utter fiasco, the party. But she had come! And he had feasted his eyes on her the whole evening long. Once he had almost touched her hand. Yes, think of that! *Almost!* Weeks may pass, months perhaps, before their paths cross again. (What if her parents took it into their heads to move to another city? Such things happen.) He tries to fix it in his memory – the way she cast her eyes, the way she talked (to others), the way she threw her head back in laughter, the way her dress clung to her slender figure. He goes through it all piece by piece, moment by moment, from the time she entered and nodded to someone behind him, not seeing him, or not recognizing him perhaps. (Or had she been too shy to respond to his eager glance?) The sort of girl who never revealed her true feelings. A mysterious and elusive creature. How little she knew, how little anyone knew, the oceanic depths of emotion which engulfed him!

To be in love. To be utterly alone . . .

Thus it begins . . . the sweetest and the bitterest sorrow that one can know, The hunger, the loneliness that precedes initiation.

In the loveliest red apple there is hidden a worm. Slowly, relendessly, the worm eats the apple away. Until there is nothing left but the worm.

And the core, that too? No, the core of the apple lingers, even if only as idea. That every apple has a core, is this not sufficient to counterbalance all uncertainty, all doubt and misgiving? What matter the world, what matter the suffering and death of untold millions, what matter if everything goes to pot – so long as *she,* the heart and core, remains! Even if he is never to see her again, he is free to think about her, speak to her in dream, love her, love her from afar, love her for ever and ever. No one can deny him that. No, no one.

Like a body composed of millions of cells, sorrow

grows and grows and grows, feeds upon itself, renews its million selves, becomes the world and all that is, or the riddle which answers to it. Everything fades but the torment. *Things are the way they are.* That is the horrible, the perpetual torment . . . And to think that one has only to do oneself in – and the riddle is solved! But *is* that a solution? Is it not slightly ridiculous? Moral suicide is so much easier. Adjusting to life, as they say. Not to what should be or ought be. *Be a man!* Later, of course, one realizes that 'to be a man' is quite another matter. The day is sure to dawn when it becomes all too clear that few there are who deserve the title: MAN. The more aware of this you become, the fewer men you find. Hold tenaciously to the thought and you end up in the void of the Himalayas, there to discover that what is called man is still waiting to be born.

In the course of making these manly adjustments to reality, the feminine world appears to undergo a prismatic deformation. It is at this point in one's development that someone comes along who has had more experience, someone 'who knows women'. This is the realistic dolt, the down-to-earth type, who believes that to sleep with a woman is to know her. By virtue of countless collisions with the other sex, something which passes for knowledge has accrued to his make-up. Something like a psychological wig, one might say.

Faced with a real woman, a real experience, this type of individual is bound to cut as ridiculous a figure as an old man trying to make himself look young. The wig becomes the focus of attention.

I remember a chap who became my boon companion during this transient period. I remember his grotesque antics with women, and how they affected me. He was always voicing the fear that to fall head over heels in love was to court disaster. Never give yourself wholly to one woman! So he made it his business to take me around. He would show me how to behave naturally, as he put it, with a woman.

The strange thing was that in the course of these adventures it happened again and again that the women he treated so cavalierly fell in love with *me*. It didn't take long to discover that the objects of his fancy weren't at all taken in by his swashbuckling behaviour. It was only too apparent, from the way these 'victims of prey' humoured him and mothered him, that he was only deluding himself in thinking that he 'had a way with women'. I saw that this 'man of the world' was just a child to them, even though in bed he could make them whinny with pleasure, or sob or groan, or cling to him with quiet desperation. He had a way of taking leave abruptly, like a coward beating a hasty retreat. 'A cunt's a cunt,' he would say, trying to conceal his panic, and then he'd scratch his head and wonder aloud if there wasn't one, just *one* cunt, who was different.

No matter how attached I became to a 'cunt', I was always more interested in the person who owned it. A cunt doesn't live a separate, independent existence. Nothing does. Everything is interrelated. Perhaps a cunt, smelly though it may be, is one of the prime symbols for the connection between all things. To enter life by way of the vagina is as good a way as any. If you enter deep enough, remain long enough, you will find what you seek. But you've got to enter with heart and soul – and check your belongings outside. (By belongings I mean – fears, prejudices, superstitions.)

The whore understands this perfectly. That's why, when shown a bit of kindness, she's ready to give her soul. Most men, when taking a whore, don't even bother to remove hat and coat, figuratively speaking. Small wonder they receive so little for their money. A whore, if treated right, can be the most generous of souls. Her one desire is to be able to give herself, not just her body.

We are all striving acquisitively – for money, love, position, honour, respect, even for divine favour. To get something for nothing seems to be the *summum bonum*. Do we not say: 'Go get yourself a fuck!' Strange locution. As if one could possibly get a fuck without giving one. Even in this basic realm of communion the notion prevails that a fuck is something to get, not to give. Or, if the opposite is stressed –*Jesus, what a fuck I gave her!* – then the thought of something received in exchange is obscured. No man or woman can boast of handing out a good fuck unless he or she is well fucked too. Otherwise one might as well talk of fucking a bag of oats. And that is precisely what goes on, for the most part. You go to the butcher with a piece of tail, and he makes a thin hash of it for you. Some are crazy enough to ask for porterhouse steak when all they want is a bit of chopped meat.

Fucky-wucky! It's not the simple pastime it would seem to be. Wonder is often expressed about the ways of primitives. Some question how it would be to use animals. (Domestic ones, to be sure.) Few are completely satisfied that they know all there is to be known about the business. Sometimes, after years of (so-called) normal sexual behaviour, a man and wife will begin experimenting. Sometimes husbands and wives exchange partners for a night, or for longer. And now and then one hears from the lips of a traveller strange tales, tales of mysterious performances, of formidable feats practised in the observance of strange forms of ritual. The masters of the art have nearly always served a rigorous spiritual apprenticeship. Self-discipline is the clue to their prowess. The man of God, in short, seems to have it over the gladiator.

Most youngsters never get the chance to enjoy the luxury of prolonged and often fruitless metaphysical speculation. They are whisked out into the world and made to assume responsibilities before they have had the opportunity to identify themselves (in the heaven of thought) with those who consumed themselves wrestling with the eternal problems. Shoving myself out prematurely, I soon realized my error and, after floundering about, I decided to give myself a break. Throwing off the harness, I made an effort to live the natural life. I failed. Back to the pavements I went and into the arms of the woman I was trying to ditch.

Throughout an interminable winter I slept at the bottom of the deep pit which I had dug for myself. I slept like a bear. And in my sleep it was the world problem which filled my dreams.

From the rear windows of the flat we occupied, my mistress and I, I could look into the bedroom of the one I loved, the one I swore to love for ever. She was married and had a child. At the time I was ignorant of the fact that she was living in this house across the yard; I never dreamt that it was *she* whose silhouette loomed before my eyes, and *me* filled with blackest misery. If only I had known, how grateful I would have been to sit for ever before the window, ay, even in muck and filth. No, never once during those agonizing sessions did I suspect that she was there, less than a stone's throw away, almost within my grasp. *Almost!* If only, when calling her name in vain, I had thought to open the window! She would have heard. She might have answered.

Crawling into bed with the other, I would pass heart-breaking hours wondering about the one who was lost to me. Exhausted, I would fall back into the deep pit. What an abominable form of suicide! I not only destroyed myself and the love that devoured me, I destroyed everything that came my way, including the one who clung to me desperately in sleep. I had to annihilate the world which had made me its victim. I was like a maniac armed with a rusty axe who swings frantically right and left. All perpetrated in the besotted trammels of sleep.

Was it I who was responsible for these dastardly acts? No! Someone, some monster of the deep, had taken possession of me. Whoever, whatever I had become, I was one who murdered without rhyme or reason. And without let. Even awake, I sometimes caught myself at it!

And every day – who would believe it? – I set forth mechanically in search of work. I might even take a job for the space of a few hours. By nightfall, however, I was always back in the lair. The moment I entered her presence a sorrowful quietude would invade me. There it was, her cunt, always open, always in wait for me. Ready, like a flower trap, to swallow me whole.

It was an ordeal which threatened never to end. Time dragged in a way I had never thought possible. There were five-minute intervals which stretched out so painfully that I thought I would go mad. The man watching the clock was shackled and gagged; inside him were a thousand different beings tugging for release. Every throttled impulse seemed to revert to a mysterious source and there take shape and substance, become a sort of elemental creature, a live and terrifying homunculus. The conflict between these embryonic selves imprisoned in my sleepwalking body took on fantastic proportions. If I went for a walk they hovered about me in a cloud, like ectoplasm generated by the mere act of breathing. During intercourse they passed out of me, as though I were emptying refuse into a sewer. The moment I opened my eyes they were back again, swarms of them, as clamorous and insistent as ever.

My only recourse – I no longer had a choice – was to lose my identity. In other words, flee from myself. In so doing I thought I was running away from *her*. I didn't get very far, either from myself or from her. I gave out that I had left for Alaska, but the truth was that I remained only a few blocks away. I behaved, however, as if I had truly disappeared. Alaska turned out to be a deep mine in which I buried myself. I remained below a long time, oblivious of such things as food, fresh air, sunlight, human companionship.

In the depths I made contact with the earth spirits. Thus I came to realize that the problems which I had situated in a vague beyond, like dreamy Zeppelins, were of subterranean essence. For company I had such vital spirits as Nietzsche, Emerson, Thoreau, Whitman, Fabre, Havelock Ellis, Maeterlinck, Strindberg, Dostoevsky, Gorky, Tolstoy, Verhaeren, Bergson, Herbert Spencer. I understood their language. I was at home with them. No valid reason why I should ever come up for air. I had the whole thing in my hands. But like a lone prospector who stumbles upon a forgotten gold mine, I had to take what I could in my bare hands and come to the surface for assistance. It was imperative to convince others that such a treasure existed, beg them to return with me and help themselves to their heart's content.

The endeavour to make known this great discovery eventually proved so difficult that I almost forgot what my purpose was in coming back to life. Not only did I meet with scepticism and ridicule, I was treated as if

I had lost my mind. My closest and dearest friends were the most impervious. Now and then I came across a stranger who gave a sympathetic ear, but for one reason or another we never met a second time. The impression left by such encounters was that we were heralds from some other world whose destiny it was to make momentary contact merely to preserve the tiny spark of faith.

By the time I was ripe for another 'love affair' I was so bruised and bewildered that I was anyone's prey. Suddenly I was plunged into the world of music. And I responded with every quivering pore. The effect was that of taking the soul to a Turkish bath. What metaphysical notions I had retained were steamed out. In the process I lost some superfluous flesh, and with the flesh a variety of skin irritations.

With this one the war of the sexes began in earnest. Her musical talent, which was the magnet of attraction, soon took second place. She was an hysterical, lascivious, puritanical bitch whose crack was hidden beneath a tangled mat of hair that looked for all the world like a sporran. The first time my fingers came in contact with it was of an evening during the early days of our courtship. She had stretched herself out on the radiator to warm up. She had nothing on but a silk dressing gown. The tuft of hair between her legs stood out so prominently that it almost looked as if she had a head of cauliflower hidden beneath her wrap. To her horror and amazement I made a grab for it. She was that startled I thought she would jump out of her skin. There was nothing for it but to grab my hat and coat, and bolt. In the hallway, at the head of the stairs, she caught up with me; she was still trembling, still dazed, but obviously unwilling to let me depart in such precipitate fashion. Under a flickering gas jet I held her in my arms and did my best to soothe her ruffled feelings. She responded with warm embraces. I concluded that everything was okey-dokey again. (A few more minutes, thought I to myself, and we'll be back in her snug little room making honey.) Unbuttoning my overcoat as discreetly as possible, I opened my fly. Then I gently took her hand and closed it around my pecker. That was the climax! With a shudder she let go of it and burst into a spasm of tears. I left her there in the hallway and, scampering down the long flight of stairs, I fled into the street. The following day I received a letter saying that she hoped never to see me again.

A few days later, however, I was back. Again she stretched out on the radiator, clad only in the silk dressing gown. This time I was a little more tactful. Casually, as it were, I ran my fingers lightly over the dressing gown. Her thick bush seemed to be full of electricity;

the hair stood up stiff and crackly, like a wire sponge. It was necessary, in this approach, to maintain a running stream of chatter about music and other lofty subjects, while stroking her in absent-minded fashion. By resorting to this dodge I enabled her, or so I surmised, to tell herself that there was no harm in such deportment. In the kitchen later she showed me a few stunts she had learnt in boarding school; these acrobatic enticements served, of course, to reveal her figure to full advantage. Every time her dressing sack fell open it disclosed the rich growth of fungus which was her secret pride. Tantalizing, to say the least.

Things went on this way for several weeks before she forgot herself. Even then she didn't abandon herself completely. The first time she lay down for it she insisted that I try to do it through her nightgown. Not only was she mortally afraid of being knocked up, she wanted to test me. Should I give in to her whims and caprices, she would be able and willing to trust me all the way. That was her logic.

Gradually, very gradually, she began to react like a normal human being. Occasionally I would pay her a call in the middle of the day. I always had to proffer the excuse that I came to hear her play. It would never do to walk in and grab hold of her immediately. If I took a seat in the corner and listened to her attentively she might stop halfway through a sonata and come over to me of her own accord, let me run my hand up her leg, and finally straddle me. With the orgasm she would sometimes have a weeping fit. Doing it in broad daylight always awakened her sense of guilt. (The way she voiced it was that it deteriorated her keyboard technique.) Anyway, the better the fuck, the *worse* she felt afterwards. 'You don't really care for *me*,' she would say. 'All you're after is sex.' By dint of repeating it a thousand times it became a fact. I was already fed up with her by the time we legalized the relationship.

A few months after our marriage her mother arrived for a brief stay. I had heard a lot about her mother, mostly derogatory things. Evidently they had never had much affection for each other. With the mother came a poodle dog, a birdcage and a couple of stout valises. Oddly enough, we hit it off from the start, the mother and I. I found her an attractive middle-aged woman, fleshy, jovial, delightfully tolerant and, though not very bright, full of understanding. I liked the way she hummed and whistled in going about the chores. In short, she was a 'natural'. Her defects, trifling to my eyes, were thoroughly human and forgivable. As I say, we got along splendidly, which was regrettable because it only made our conjugal life that much more difficult.

When the mother's stay drew to a close we had to promise that we would return the visit soon. 'Make it a honeymoon trip,' she said laughingly.

To me the thought of a vacation, no matter what the excuse, was elating. To make it a reality I knew that I would have to pretend disinterest.

My tactics were so successful that before long I had the secret pleasure of listening to my wife pleading and coaxing me to go.

Her mother's place was like a doll's house: everything spick and span, dainty, bright, cheerful. The city itself was beautiful, the neighbours friendly and hospitable. I found her father a simple, easygoing fellow who accepted me immediately and made me feel at ease.

It began most promisingly, the honeymoon.

Mornings we would lie abed all hours, the sun streaming in through the open windows, the birds singing madly, the flowers in full bloom, and in the kitchen – we had just to give the word – the bacon and eggs sizzling in the pan. The feeling of jealousy which the mother had unwittingly aroused during her stay with us seemed to have vanished. The daughter gave herself up to the fucking wholeheartedly, quite as if the fact of being under the parental roof had bestowed some long-awaited absolution. For a prudish bitch such as she was, she certainly gave herself free rein. At times

I had the feeling that she was throwing herself at me just to prove to her mother that she possessed as great a sexual attraction as any other female, her mother included. She even carried on flirtatiously with her mother's friends, a little group of lusty cavaliers who were ever at the mother's beck and call. She seemed to have forgotten that I had ever looked at her mother with an approving eye. She grew so carefree, in fact, that now and then she would leave me for hours on end, leave me alone with her mother, while she gallivanted about town.

The inevitable happened, of course. One morning, when she had left us alone, the mother decided to take a bath. I was sitting in the parlour, still in my pyjamas, lazily scanning the morning paper. It was a warm, sunny day and the birds were chirping like wild. I could hear her mother splashing about in the tub while humming to herself in that enchanting niggerish way which always stirred my blood. I got to thinking about her so strongly that my hands began to tremble. Suddenly I heard her calling, calling for a towel. I fetched the towel, rubbed her down from head to foot, then picked her up and carried her to the bedroom. She was a marvellous piece of tail, needless to say.

Now the honeymoon was really under way. I was honeymooning it all over the place, first with the daughter, then with the mother. All went smoothly for a while, everyone in the best of spirits. Then, overnight it seemed, my wife grew suspicious. She was determined that we return home at once. Naturally I didn't evince much enthusiasm over this prospect. The bickering and chaffering recommenced, grew disgustingly acrimonious.

We quarrelled so bitterly that finally we decided to separate. She would go her way, I mine. We left the house together and at the end of the block we said goodbye to one another and departed in opposite directions.

A few days later, while strolling down the main street of a nearby town, I ran smack into her. She began to weep right there in the street, declaring that I had never loved her, never. In the next breath she begged me to accompany her to the room she had taken in a lodging house. She wanted to talk things over, she said. She made it sound as if it were most imperative. Knowing what a son of a bitch I had been, I consented. (Not that I thought we would get anywhere.)

To my surprise she said nothing about her mother; she talked only about herself, what a miserable life she had had and how nobody had ever understood her. She said she wanted love, not sex, and with that we fell into a clutch. When it was over we continued to lie where we had rolled – under the table. Her eyes were red and swollen, her hair was down in a tangled mass. She looked the image of grief and hysteria. Again she started in about herself, her poor misunderstood self. Wanted to know if I thought she was 'a bad sort'. It sounded so ridiculous, coming from her mouth, that I didn't know what to answer. Then she began about her mother, how she had always feared that one day she would behave just like her. She begged me to admit that her mother was no good, forced me to promise that we would never see her again, which I did readily enough, adding that there was nothing to be disturbed about, that her fears were groundless, and so on. Soothing syrup, in other words.

Back home again she made the alarming discovery that she was pregnant. This brought on a severe depression. She didn't want to have a child, not yet, at any rate. She didn't want an abortion either. She was frightened stiff. Frightened of everything, it seemed to me.

In desperation I suggested that we consult her cousin, whom I had met once and rather liked. Alice, as her cousin was called, had a realistic approach to life. According to my wife, she was another 'no good sort', but in a pinch one couldn't be too fussy.

We had no trouble persuading Alice to lend her services. She came at once, and with her she brought a box of big black pills, an age-old remedy. There were mustard baths to be taken with the pills, and this and that.

It was a sweltering summer's evening when Alice arrived. The three of us had stripped down and were seated in the dark over a pitcher of beer, joking about the situation. Under the influence of the warm beer Alice soon threw off all restraint. She sat in my lap and began kissing me passionately. I had to beg my wife to pull her away.

By the time Alice passed out my wife was ready to strangle her. As for the pills, she refused to touch them.

The longer we lived together the worse it got. We had started out on the wrong foot and nothing could ever right the situation. Every friend or acquaintance my wife had was destined to betray her. Her pride and suspiciousness egged me on. Even when I took the baby out in the perambulator she kept her eye on me. She had good reason, I must admit, to be ever on the watch. Often I would leave the house, innocent like, with the baby carriage, to keep an appointment with one of her friends. Sometimes I'd park the carriage outside an apartment house and take her friend inside, under the stairs, for a quickie. Or, if there was a gathering at the house, I would go off with one of her friends to buy food or drink, and on the way I'd stand her up against a fence and do what I could. If I hadn't finally been caught with my pants down I think I'd have driven the poor woman stark mad. It was truly abominable the way I treated her, but I was simply powerless to act otherwise. There was something about her which inspired the most contemptible conduct.

The strange thing about her was that when she wished to make herself seductive she could do it most effectively. She would have made a good striptease artist. After the divorce, when I made weekly visits to hand over the alimony, she grew even more enticing. She was always about to get dressed just when I arrived, or making ready to take a bath, or else coming out of the bath to repose a few moments on the divan, clad of course in one of her attractive silk kimonos.

We got along better after the divorce. At least we were able to converse. We were also able to display a touch of sympathy as well as a sense of humour. It was like a state of permanent truce. To an outsider it might well have looked as if we were courting one another all over again. There was this difference however: when I first courted her she had behaved like a prude; now, though still withholding herself, she deployed her sexual charms skilfully. For example, when she brushed a crumb off my fly she no longer jumped away in fright on discovering that I had an erection. Now she might even go so far as to give it a playful squeeze, remarking in her brittle way while doing so that there was nothing doing, but saying it in a cheerful and not too casual way, as though to imply that if I were real good, that is, if I stood on my hind legs and begged for it properly, she might permit certain liberties which I had no rightful reason to suppose she would grant. It was most important to remember to act delicately. (Touch it, if you like, but do it like a gentleman!) No, I was not to think that because we had once been man and wife I could treat her like a pushover.

Naturally, after hours of this kind of heavy flirtation things would get rather involved. Little by little we would go over her anatomy together, explore every portion of it. It might be a bump on her thigh that needed inspection, or maybe she was broadening too much, would I mind feeling her buttocks, weighing them in my hands or some such nonsense, all dragged out at great length and with a mixture, on her part, of real and assumed coyness. I had to know just how to look at her, how to touch her, how to weigh her breasts or the heavy cheeks of her butt. If I handled the calf of her leg with proper feeling – or should we say with respect? – she might raise her gown and permit me to run my hands over her fleshy thighs. But if I made the mistake of grabbing that bush of hers without due preliminaries she would pull the curtain down for the day.

It was tantalizing and demoralizing. Worse than that, because the child whom I came expressly to see was usually quickly dismissed. Occasionally, too, the child would suddenly return to find us in the midst of a passionate struggle. There was something cunning and malign about these manoeuvrings. Just as she had learnt to mobilize her sex, so she had learnt to mobilize the child. I wanted the child and I wanted that bushy cunt of hers which she was forever dangling before my eyes like a piece of bait.

Worst of all was the leave-taking. Every time I made ready to leave, the ground seemed to give way beneath her. In the vestibule, saying goodbye, she always seemed ready for anything. What she hoped each time, I suppose, was that I would relinquish the other woman and resume life with her, even if it didn't hold too much promise. The fact that we were still sexually drawn to each other only added to her confusion and desperation. When it came to the farewell kiss in the darkness of the vestibule the tension became excruciating. I could do anything to her – except slip it in. Locked in each other's arms, we would stand there interminably, groaning, gasping, chewing each other alive. Sometimes she would insist that I wash myself. A strange piece of thoughtfulness! As if to say – you don't want to be caught red-handed! She'd stand there at the sink, solicitously observing the performance, and with a sort of ethereal motion nervously brush my coat.

During one of these prolonged bouts in the vestibule – the last! – she was seized with such violent emotion that suddenly she burst into sobs, horrible sobs, and pushing me from her with all her strength, she fled inside and threw herself on the floor. Unable to move from the spot, I listened in terror to her wild and uncontrollable outburst, I was on the point of rushing to her, of making abject surrender. ('I'll do anything, *anything*, only in the name of God, stop it!') I stood thus a few moments, irresolute fortunately, but shaken to the roots.

In those few moments I lived out a complete martyrdom.

She must have known that I was wavering, must have exerted every ounce of will to hold me. But she failed.

'Forwards!' I said to myself. 'Forwards at all costs!'

And with that I bolted. In the street I broke into a run, still fearful that she would pull me back. I ran with tears streaming down my face.

Nearing home I had another spell of tears, this time for joy. Joy that I had found the one I truly loved. Joy that I had entered upon a new life. The image of grief and hysteria writhing on the floor receded. It had happened aeons ago, in some other life. I could think only of the one who was waiting for me.

Passing a florist I debated whether or not to select a bunch of violets.

As I climbed the stoop I kept repeating to myself: 'Never again! Never again!'

Opening the door, I called her name. No answer. A lamp was burning on the little table. Underneath the lamp a piece of paper showed. I knew immediately that something was amiss.

It was just as I thought. A brief note, saying that she would be gone for a few days, couldn't stand it any longer. I was not to try to reach her; she would return as soon as she had regained her courage. No reproaches.

I slid into a chair, clasping the note which I now knew by heart. To my astonishment I was void of feeling. I was completely numb, in fact. All I could do was to stare vacantly at the wall, I might have sat like that indefinitely. I might have turned into a rock, I was that drained of thought, will or emotion.

Suddenly I sensed that I was not alone. Plantlike, I slowly shifted my gaze. There she stood, framed in the doorway. For several long moments she stood with one hand clutching the doorknob, as though fixing the picture once and for all in her mind. Then impulsively she rushed to my side and flung herself at my feet.

There were no words. We simply gazed into each other's eyes. A long, long time it lasted: a silence more eloquent than any I have ever known. All that we were powerless to utter voiced itself in this frantic mute exchange.

I have no recollection of ever coming out of this trance performance. Were it possible at this moment to return to the scene, I am certain we would still be there, the two of us, our eyes torn from their sockets, hers glued to mine, mine glued to hers.

With the jump to Paris the whole picture changed. Men and women everywhere, but together. Good food, good wines, good beds. The boulevards, the cafés, the markets, the parks, the bridges, the bookstalls. And conversation! And benches to rest your bones. And time to dream, if you wished . . .

The first thing one notices, in Paris, is that sex is in the air. Wherever you go, whatever you do, you usually find a woman beside you. Women are everywhere, like flowers. It makes one feel good, feel like one's old self again. One melts down, burrows into the earth, glows like a glow-worm.

The sexual promiscuity which Americans indulge in doesn't seem to make them light-hearted. It doesn't open them up. How strange to hear Americans discussing the French female! As if they were all budding harlots. How confused they are concerning the true relation between love and sex!

A Frenchman would not be ashamed to admit that he had fallen in love with a whore. It might drive him nuts eventually, but he would never think about the situation the way an American does. If he went gaga it would be because of love, not because of moral scruples. The American, on the other hand, can emancipate himself in such studied, deliberate fashion as to be oblivious of everything a woman has to offer except her body. He will treat an exceptional woman like a whore and fall madly in love with a nitwit. Or, a prey to sentimentality, he may treat a whore like a queen, clap or no clap. He may even rule love out of his life altogether, for fear of seeming romantic. What frightens the shit out of him is to give himself body and soul. The American woman, consequently, is frequently a love-starved creature, clamouring for the moon. She will make a man work himself to the bone to satisfy her silly whims. Given free rein, she becomes truly insatiable.

Paris is one of those places where the American female prowls about like a cat in heat. She may be looking for love, but she'll settle for sex any time. The foreigner adds a spice to the dish which she never tasted before. He can give the illusion of love and make it seem satisfying. I once knew an American opera singer in Paris who had fallen in love with a young Turk. She knew that he was fucking her only because of the money she lavished on him, but she liked him, she liked the way he treated her when he made love to her. She had a husband who she said was kind and thoughtful, but he had never been much of a lover. Not that he was indifferent or impotent. No, he really cared for her, and in his naive way he probably believed that she cared for him. He was not unaware of what it was that impelled her to go abroad twice a year. He simply closed his eyes to the truth.

A man like that is sometimes spoken of as a considerate devil. To my mind he is just a self-deluded pimp. Whatever may be said against the wife of such an individual only evokes one's sympathy. Given half a chance, a woman offers her whole being. It's instinctive with her. Not man! A man is usually plagued with all kinds of disturbing notions with regard to love, sex, politics, art, religion and so on. A man is always more muddled than a woman. He needs woman if for no other purpose than to be straightened out. Sometimes it takes nothing more than a good, clean, healthy fuck to do the trick. Yes, sometimes an honest fuck is all that it needs to dissipate the notion that directing world affairs isn't exclusively *his* responsibility. Men have a way of taking things seriously rather than tragically. They are always looking beyond their noses for something more important than what's to hand. Love, when it occurs, is something to be carried on in the wings, as it were. For them the real drama is always taking place on the world stage.

The drama of partnership, which is every man's drama and a most vital one, only penetrates the consciousness of the male when faced with divorce. If he has borne the brunt of the battle, he is apt to liken marriage to a living hell. He has to generalize about it, make it a world problem. If the woman was the one to suffer, he will maintain that she didn't understand him, or that she was all crossed up. Or he may shift the blame to our faulty economic system. Few men seem capable of viewing their relationship with the opposite sex as a creative struggle. (The circle, and in it just yin and yang – how wonderful!) Yes, love is the magnet which brings two opposites together. What is to hold them together, that no one asks. Love will take care of itself. And it does – by dying a natural death.

Let us not speak of the derelicts of love! Any Sunday, on the boulevard, you may see them dragging behind . . . so many tin cans attached to the parental tails.

Love is the drama of completion, of unification.

Personal and boundless, it leads to deliverance from the tyranny of the ego. Sex is impersonal, and may or may not be identified with love. Sex can strengthen and deepen love, or work destructively.

To me it seems that sex was best understood, best expressed, in the pagan world, in the world of the primitives and in the religious world. In the first it was exalted on the aesthetic plane, in the second on the magical plane and in the third on the spiritual plane. In our world, where only the bestial level obtains, sex functions in a void.

We are becoming more and more neuter, more and more asexual. The increasing variety of perverse crimes bears eloquent testimony to the fact. The killer, as pathological specimen, is an alarming offshoot of the degenerate breed which is constantly undermining the social fabric. Emotionally thwarted, he can only make contact with his fellow man by spilling his blood.

There are all kinds of killers among us. The type who finds his way to the electric chair is but the forerunner of a frightening host which is ever on the increase. In a sense we are all killers. Our whole way of life is rooted in mutual slaughter. Never has there been a world so avid for security, and never has life been more insecure. To protect ourselves, we invent the most fantastic instruments of destruction, which prove to be boomerangs. No one seems to believe in the power of love, the only dependable power. No one believes in his neighbour, or in himself, let alone a supreme being. Fear, envy, suspicion are rampant everywhere. Ergo, fuck your brains out while there is still time!

For some sex leads to sainthood; for others it is the road to hell. In this respect it is like everything else in life – a person, a thing, an event, a relationship. All depends on one's point of view. To make life more beautiful, more wonderful, more deep and satisfying, we must gaze with fresh, clear vision upon every contributing element of life. If there is something wrong about our attitude towards sex then there is something wrong about our attitude towards bread, towards money, towards work, towards play, towards everything. How can one enjoy a good sex life if he has a distorted, unhealthy attitude towards other aspects of life?

It is difficult, almost absurd, to tell emotional cripples that self-expression is the all-important. Not what is expressed nor how, but just expressing oneself. One feels like urging them to try anything if it will further self-liberation. There is nothing in itself, we have been told time and again, which is wrong or evil. It is the fear of doing wrong, the fear of committing this or that act, which is wrong. 'Fear is not to sow because of the birds.'

Today we seem animated almost exclusively by fear. We fear even that which is good, that which is healthy, that which is joyous. And what is the hero? Primarily one who has conquered his fears. One can be a hero in any realm; we never fail to recognize him when he appears. His singular virtue is that he has become one with life, one with himself. Having ceased to doubt and question, he quickens the flow and the rhythm of life. The coward, *par contre,** seeks to arrest life's flow. He arrests nothing, to be sure, unless it be himself. Life moves on, whether we act as cowards or as heroes. Life has no other discipline to impose, if we would but realize it, than to accept life unquestioningly. Everything we shut our eyes to, everything we run away from, everything we deny, denigrate or despise, serves to defeat us in the end. What seems nasty, painful, evil, can become a source of beauty, joy and strength, if faced with open mind. Every moment is a golden one for him who has the vision to recognize it as such. Life is now, every moment, no matter if the world be full of death. Death triumphs only in the service of life.

In reading my books, which are purely autobiographical, one should bear in mind that I write with one foot in the past. In telling the story of my life I have frequently discarded the chronological sequence in favour of the circular or spiral form of progression. The time sequence which relates one event to another in linear fashion strikes me as falsely imitative of the true rhythm of life. The facts and events which form the chain of one's life are but starting points along the path of self-discovery. I have endeavoured to plot the inner pattern, follow the potential being who was constantly deflected from his course, who circled around himself, was becalmed for long stretches, sank to the bottom or vainly essayed to reach the lonely, desolate summits. I have tried to capture the quintessential moments wherein whatever happened produced profound alterations. The man telling the story is no longer the one who experienced the events recorded. Distortion and deformation are unavoidable in the reliving of one's life. The inner purpose of such disfigurement, of course, is to seize the true reality of things and events. Thus, for no *apparent* reason, I revert now and then to a period not only anterior but unrelated to the one in hand. The puzzled reader may well wonder if these switchbacks are not the work of caprice. Who can say? To my mind, they have the same *raison d'être* as all invention. Devices, certainly, but to analyze them gets one nowhere. A sudden switch, a long parenthetical detour, a crazy monologue, an excursus, a remembrance cropping out like a cliff in fog – their very instantaneity kills all speculation.

No one takes a straight-cut line through life. Often we fail to stop at the stations indicated on the timetable. Sometimes we go off the track. Sometimes we lose our way, or take to the air and vanish like chaff. The most tremendous voyages are sometimes taken without moving from the spot. In the space of a few minutes some individuals live out the span of an ordinary mortal's total experience. Some use up numbers of lives in the course of their stay here below. Some burgeon like mushrooms whilst others slip back hopelessly, mired in their tracks. What it is that goes on moment by moment in a man's life is for ever unfathomable. No man can possibly relate the whole story, no matter how limited a fragment of his life he may choose to dwell on.

It is this aura of the unknown, in which the real struggle takes place, that alone interests me. In describing facts, events, relationships, even trivia, I am constantly endeavouring to make the reader aware of the all-pervasiveness of that dark, mysterious realm *in the absence of which nothing could happen.* Even when I first began to write I was aware of this which I have alluded to, but in a vague, confused way. I knew that not only my own life but every man's is interesting (a weak word!) if one takes the trouble to delve into it. I realized that the telling of it had importance (false word) because instructive – to myself and to others like or unlike me. After all, the art of telling is only another form of communion. But despite – or was it because of – my seriousness, my persistence and assiduity, all I succeeded in producing were a few abortions, which fortunately were never published. During this period of apprenticeship, events piled up with such speed and in such number that the writer in me was completely submerged. Everything I wrote up to the *Tropic of Capricorn* was, as I now see it, an effort to get started, an effort to begin the long delayed 'confession'. In other words, so much ice-breaking.

There was just one book I always wanted to write. The plan of this work I mapped out long ago during a period of extreme anguish. Throughout all my wanderings I managed to hold on to these notes. Extraordinary, indeed, for time and again I was stripped of everything. Even had I lost the notes, it would not have mattered: everything that ever happened to me had been burnt into my brain. The writing of this one and only work has been going on for many, many years – the greater part of it in my head. Thus far, all but the final volume has appeared in print. How the final edifice will shape itself I still do not know.

Living it over and over again, I see that what stands out are *moments*, not facts. Moments and places, and often looks – certain unforgettable expressions which the human countenance registers only once or twice in a lifetime. As for chronology, cause and event, the record remains, like history itself, confused and baffling. Everyone writes his own history of world events. If it were possible to compare accounts, we would be dismayed to discover that the historical has neither reality nor authenticity, that the past, private or universal, is an impenetrable jungle.

With the biographical record it is much the same. Our meanderings form a labyrinth capable of endless interpretations. Few ever reach the heart of the labyrinth. To confront the Minotaur, and slay him, is to be slain. Thus the past is scotched, and the future too. Nothing that happened, nothing that may happen or will happen, any longer has importance enough to weigh us down. To recount a heartbreaking incident becomes as joyous an affair as a good bowel movement – or a trip to the moon. Why tell anything then? Why continue? Because it is a gratuitous pleasure. To lead a life divorced from books and the making of books, to live without sex, without human companionship, is it so dreadful? Even a writer can do it, if he knows how to live with himself. That is what I mean: I have learnt to live with myself. And like it.*

We go our way picturing the world to be thus and so. We move unthinkingly against a panorama which changes kaleidoscopically. And as we drag along we carry with us dead images of live moments in the past. Until the day we meet *her*. Suddenly the world is no longer the same. *Everything* has altered. But how can the world be altered in the wink of an eye? It is an experience we all know, yet it brings us no closer to truth. We go on knocking at the door . . .

Once I saw a portrait of Rubens as he looked when he married his young wife. They were portrayed together, she seated and he upright behind her. Never can I forget the emotion this picture inspired. I had one long deep look into the world of contentment. I could feel the vigour of Rubens, then in the prime of life; I could feel the confidence which his very young and very lovely mate awakened in him. I sensed that some overpowering inner event had occurred which Rubens the painter had striven to fix for ever in this picture of conjugal bliss. Not knowing the story of his life, I do not know whether he lived happily with her ever afterwards or not. What happened subsequent to the moment recorded is of no importance to me. My interest lies wholly in that moment which was so moving and inspiring to me. It remains imperishable in my mind.

Similarly I know that certain things which I have recorded in word are true and imperishable. What happened to me or to 'her' subsequently is of little importance.

Sometimes the recital of a bald sexual incident is of great moment, laden with unimaginable significance. The cold fire of sex burns in us like a sun; it is never completely extinguished. Thus it is perhaps that a naked description of the physical embrace can sometimes transport us to a state transcending the erotic, can create in us the illusion of being hidden from the sight of the all-seeing one, if only for a few breathless moments.

If we stopped to think about the ceaseless activity which informs the earth and the heavens about us, would we ever give ourselves up to thoughts of death? If we deeply realized that even in death this frenzied activity proceeds ceaselessly and remorselessly, would we withhold ourselves in any way? The gods of old came down to earth to mingle with humankind, to fornicate with animals and trees and with the elements themselves. Why are we so full of restraint? Why do we not give in all directions? Is it fear of losing ourselves? Until we do lose ourselves there can be no hope of finding ourselves. We are of the world, and to enter fully into the world we must first lose ourselves in it. The path to heaven leads through hell, it is said. What path we take is of no importance, as long as we cease to tread cautiously.

Sex and death: I notice how frequently I couple them. Whenever I try to summon a time when life was truly pullulating I think of the Middle Ages. Never, in our western history, was there a period in which death was so rife and life so full and rich. For three centuries Europe was devastated by 'the Black Death'. The result? For one thing, a tremendous religious fervour. For another, an erotic upheaval. Fornication without let. Men and women storming heaven with their sexual gear. *Immoral?* What an empty word! The spirit of man, faced with the ever-present image of death, spilt over. Strike deep and the poorest of creatures responds. 'For the poet, the final ecstasy does not lead into the daylight of God, but into the nocturnal darkness of passion.' Sometimes life itself takes over, writes its own poem of ecstasy, signed 'Death'.

With the Renaissance came an eruption of monster-geniuses. The ferment which in the Middle Ages had been partially canalized (by the communal-religious life) broke out like a pox. The individual ran amok. Studying the portraits of the great figures of the Renaissance, the monsters spawned by Church and State, one cannot help but be impressed by the malevolence depicted in these countenances. In the ceaseless intestinal welfare which flourished, assassination was the order of the day. Incestuous love, especially in the high places, was common. And with it, of course, the poisoned dagger. Towards the end of the English Renaissance this theme came to poignant expression in the superb tragedy by John Ford: *'Tis Pity She's a Whore.* The Renaissance individual here gasps his last.

Today the individual is virtually extinct. Today we have the robot, end product of the machine age. Man functioning as a cog in a machine over which he has no control. The gat which the gangster employs, secure in the upholstered fortress of his limousine, is symbolic of the emotional vacuum in which murders are now perpetrated. The victim is no longer a single target; he and all who stand in the way of the killer are sprayed out of existence. What a contrast to the Ford play, in which a simpleton is dirked in the dark, mistaken for someone else. The effect produced by this haphazard murder is greater than that caused by the other killings which strew the play. One is outraged by the needless death – even of a fool.

Today whole populations are driven from their homes or wiped out, and the world, if moved, is powerless to intervene. Today the suffering of millions has less power to ravage us than the burning of a zoo. The world is paralysed with fear and dread. The man of long-range calculation, the deified robot, is in the saddle. It is his role, his mission, apparently, to destroy itself, namely society.

Nothing that comes to pass these next few years will surprise me in the least. When the white American killer rises up on his hind legs and begins to spit and claw, Europe, that age-old scene of carnage, will seem like a haven of peace. When the dykes give way, and they are giving way fast, nothing will be too fantastic or devilish – too unspeakable, in a word – for us to enact. Even now the look on the American face is a perverted one. Particularly in the cities. Whenever I enter the lounge of a palatial cinema – one of the few places one can find peace and solitude in a big city – I am overwhelmed by the complete lack of relationship between the ambiance of these sumptuous places of retreat and the mentality of those who laboured to produce it. Often, glancing at the man standing beside me in the urinals, a cold shudder has run up and down my spine.

Strange places, these underground retreats. Dulled and doped, one feels that if he were to remove his clothes and sit naked on one of the great plush thrones which line the walls no one would take notice, no disturbance would ensue. Often I have imagined a scene like this . . . A man, any ordinary man, seated on his throne quietly reading the newspaper; in his mouth a dead cigar. He reads for a while, then triggers the gun concealed behind the paper he is reading – and the fellow opposite him who was gazing at *Venus Anadyomene* drops dead. Rising to his feet unhurriedly, the killer saunters off, carefully folding the newspaper with its burnt hole, and as he mounts to the street he nonchalantly sticks it under his arm. At once he is lost in the crowd. Presently he stops at a cafeteria to get himself a coffee and a wholewheat doughnut. (He too believes that wholewheat is better for the intestinal tract than ordinary white flour.) Mindful of his heart, he takes his coffee weak. Down the street a few yards he spies a cravat in a shop window. The sort he had been looking for all winter. He steps in and buys a dozen. Since it's not too late – he doesn't sleep well – he makes for a billiard parlour. Almost there, he changes his mind. Would rather see *Gone With the Wind* . . .

These birds also have a sexual life. The best that money can buy. Sex is the hors d'oeuvre which they swallow between hauls. The moll gets the cocktail, and if it goes to her head, then the axe. No room in this world for hysterical blondes who double-cross you as soon as your back is turned. One's only friend is the loot. Money! Money to burn! Money means power. Power means getting away with murder. Murder means life. Ergo, don't fuck your brains away!

And now a word or two (a rock in the fog of remembrance) about Fifty-Second Street. It was on my way home the other night, just seventeen years ago, that I noticed a place called 'The Torch'. The word 'torch' struck me as having an ugly ring. (Maybe I was in a savage mood.) It set me to thinking of Paris, of the rue du Faubourg Montmartre. I thought to myself that, even if the French were to employ the word 'torch' to designate a nightspot, it would not have the same connotation as here. They might even name a joint 'The Burning Prick' in the Faubourg Montmartre, without it provoking too much comment. If there were a spot called 'The Burning Prick' in Paris, the chances are that it would be a gay and relatively innocent place. It might be crowded with whores and pimps and gigolos, but you wouldn't feel uneasy there. Even dripping with sperm, it would seem natural and fairly wholesome, all things considered. Possibly 'The Torch' is also a gay and innocuous spot, but I have my doubts. I don't like the word. I don't like stumbling into a dive and finding a hard-boiled American female with a red wig and a whisky voice spouting songs that are meant to burn you up. I don't like the idea of getting all steamed up and then discovering that you have to drop a cool hundred or so before getting anywhere near the fire. I loathe torch singers who turn sentimental when it's time to deliver the goods. It burns me up to think that a 'body electric' can insulate itself at will. It makes one feel like a maniac fighting his way through asbestos.

I may be wrong. It may be just a quiet, harmless place with soft lights, crooning voices, and palms smooth as silk in which to deposit century notes.

When I think of my evening strolls through the supposedly sinister streets of Paris – the rue Pigalle, the rue Fontaine, the rue du Faubourg Montmartre and suchlike, how very innocent it all seems now! (Like the jackass saying to the donkey: 'In the cool of the evening, when the fucking begins, I'll be there!') Sure, there were whorehouses everywhere, and on the streets and in the cafés the whores were clustered thick as rhinestones. Maybe there were stick-up men and dope peddlers too. Yet it was different . . . *don't ask me why!* At a bar the whore standing beside you might take it into her head to raise her skirt and show you her pussy, ask you to stroke it appraisingly. No riot would ensue. At most, a mild reprimand from the ogress leaning over the cashier's desk. It was permitted to examine and handle merchandise before buying. Fair and square, what? You might have the desire, and act on it, to reach into an attractive bosom and fondle a pair of appetizing teats, while the owner of this commodity poured a light lager down her throat. No one would take offence. Walking her to a nearby hotel, the one with the bubs, she might request you to pause a moment while she squatted in the street to make pee-pee. Should an *agent* happen along, he might bawl her out, but he wouldn't run her in. The sight of a woman exposing herself in public wouldn't put him in a lather. Nor was there anything to hinder you should you decide to take a half-dozen women with you to a hotel room, provided you made no fuss about the extra charge for soap and towels. The *patronne** might even give you an approving eye in showing you to a room . . . I can't imagine anything like that taking place on Fifty-Second Street amidst the flaming torches, the brown derbies and the onyx-topped tables. I can, however, imagine worse things happening there, if you know what I mean . . .

It has often been predicted that a new and higher type of man will one day make his appearance on this continent. If so, it will have to be from new shoots. The present stock may make a rich compost but it will never yield a new race. Riding the subways of New York, I see the new generation which has sprung up during my absence, the young who have come to manhood and are already reproducing their kind. I look at them as I would at so many guinea pigs. Still performing the same old tricks. In their faces is written hopelessness. They were doomed from birth. Sad to reflect, the better the conditions the worse their lot. One may teach them how to breed bigger, healthier-looking youngsters, but they and their progeny are marked as sacrificial pawns in a meaningless experiment. From generation to generation it will continue, until one lone creature escapes the hands of the vivisectionist and starts a world of his own. It will take a very, very cunning creature to make the escape. The chances are a thousand to one against it. The chances are that the guinea pigs *and* their vivisectionists will be wiped out long before. The chances are that some strange, unheard-of creature, some forgotten *homo naturalis*, will take over. One, let us say, for whom all our progress and invention mean absolutely nothing. One who will make his abode in trees or caves – and cultivate such a fucking lazy streak that maybe he will be swallowed up in his own shit.

Bravo! I say, speaking strictly for myself. Let him prove to be the filthiest bastard that ever stalked this continent, not a murmur from me! If he demonstrated nothing more than the ability to live and enjoy life without said bloody, bleeding 'progress and invention', I would hail him triumphantly. He would indeed be an exceptional type who could convince us that life, here on this continent or anywhere on earth, can be pursued without drudgery and degradation, without recourse to torture, persecution, lethal weapons and so on.

I believe it must one day come to pass. We have tried all the other ways, and we have been brought back again and again to a state of utter misery, utter helplessness.

A radical transformation might well begin here on this broad continent, for this is the crucible, the fiery furnace in which the soul of man is being tried to the utmost. If Europe is playing a losing game, we are playing a still more perilous one. We are nearer the end, further gone in every respect.

Above the national and racial dramas which are convulsing the world a greater drama is being staged: the world drama. Whether its component members participate or not, every soul alive is involved. It is no longer history which is being made; the present conflagration will rage until the old order of man is liquidated. It matters little if the current war, hot or cold, ends tomorrow or fifty years hence. There will be more wars to come, each more terrible than the last. Until the whole rotting edifice is completely demolished. Until we *(homo sapiens)* are no more.

When I first wrote these pages (1940), I was fresh from a world long-buried, a world so very different from any we know, that its quondam existence belongs more to legend than to reality. Amid the ruins which now spell Knossus and Mycenae I could dimly imagine what that other way of life might have been which men lived in the fabulous past. That it could ever have died out is almost impossible to believe. That almost nothing of the glorious spirit which animated these ancestors of ours activates us is something still more difficult to grasp. That there were more wonderful epochs still than any we know of, I for one do not doubt. Though all trace of them is at present lost, we carry the remembrance of them in our blood.

It is my conviction that what we choose to call civilization did not begin at any of those points in time which our savants, with their limited knowledge and understanding, fix upon as dawns. I see no end and no beginning anywhere. I see life and death advancing simultaneously, like twins joined at the waist. I see that at no matter what stage of evolution or devolution, no matter what the conditions, the climate, the weather, no matter whether there be peace or war, ignorance or culture, idolatry or spirituality, there is only and always the struggle of the individual, his triumph or defeat, his emancipation or enslavement, his liberation or liquidation. This struggle, whose nature is cosmic, defies all analysis, whether scientific, metaphysical, religious or historical.

The sexual drama is a partial aspect of the greater drama perpetually enacted in the soul of man. As the individual becomes more integrated, more unified, the sex problem falls into its proper perspective. The genitals are impressed, so to speak, into the service of the whole being. There is simultaneous procreation in all spheres. What is new, original and fecund issues only from a complete entity. One can fuck not only with heart and soul, as we say, but as a new being. A new being is a product of mind, created through desire, love and atonement, not through gestation in the womb. The as yet unborn are all around us, locked in the womb of time; when our hunger for true life deepens we feel their presence and make way for their coming.

Over and over I have stated that there is no way out of the present impasse. Patching things up is futile. There must be a new life from the roots.

All goes hand in hand. Sanity keeps no truck with compromise and artificiality. If we live like weasels, we fuck like weasels; if we behave like monsters, we die like monsters. Now we eat, sleep, work, play – and even fuck! – like automatons. It is the land of nod, with everyone spinning like tops.

To live one must not only be awake but awakened. If we were truly awake we would be stunned by the horror of everyday life. No one in his right senses could possibly do the crazy things which are now demanded of us every moment of the day. We are all victims, whether on top, at the bottom or in the middle. There is no escape, no immunity.

'One must live quite apart, forgetting,' said Lawrence. He tried it and failed. One cannot live apart, nor can one forget.

Now and then, in the long course of human history, an individual *has* succeeded in breaking loose and following his own unique way of life. But how rare a spectacle! Only a handful – think of it! – have ever broken the mould.

Even more tragic, more ironic, is the example of the imitators, who never tried to lead their own lives but slavishly copied the masters. Clear as the few great examples have been, even the boldest spirits have failed to understand. To follow, not to lead, that is man's curse.

It is this mere handful of exemplars who, despite our failure to comprehend, have most profoundly affected the course of human life. Studying the pattern of their lives, we observe the human spirit in revolt, emancipating itself from the thrall of illusion and delusion.

Not to go the full length, that is man's fatal error. As Jean Guehennó puts it: *'La vraie trahison est de suivre le monde comme il va, et d'employer l'esprit à le justifier.'**

Only when we fix our gaze upon these volcanic figures can we begin to estimate the pressure of the death-like forces which have us in their grip. Only then do we realize what it takes of courage and imagination, of daring and humility, to pierce the strangling web of despair and defeat which envelops us. There is no comfort or solace to be compared with that offered by the example of these few rare spirits.

Despite all the setbacks which history records, despite the rise and fall of civilizations, despite the disappearance of races and continents, some invincible and sustaining edifice, which is man's true habitation, exists. When we realize it, we will enter. We will not have to tear the world down first.

Just as rivers are swallowed up by the ocean, so all the lesser ways must yield eventually to the greater way, call it what you will. Moralities, ethics, laws, customs, beliefs, doctrines – these are of trifling import. All that matters is that the miraculous become the norm. Even now, thwarted and frustrated though we be, the miraculous is never wholly absent. But how grotesque, how awkward and clumsy are our efforts to induce it. All the ingenuity, all the heartbreaking labour spent on inventions, which are looked upon as wonder-working marvels, must be considered not only as sheer waste but as unconscious effort on man's part to forestall and evade the miraculous. We clutter the earth with our inventions, never dreaming that possibly they are unnecessary – or disadvantageous. We devise astounding means of communication, but do we communicate with one another? We move our bodies to and fro at incredible speeds, but do we really leave the spot we started from? Mentally, morally, spiritually, we are fettered. What have we achieved in moving down mountain ranges, harnessing the energy of mighty rivers, or moving whole populations about like chess pieces, if we ourselves remain the same restless, miserable, frustrated creatures we were before? To call such activity progress is utter delusion. We may succeed in altering the face of the earth until it is unrecognizable even to the Creator, but if we are unaffected wherein lies the meaning?

Meaningful acts require no stir. When things are going to wrack and ruin the most purposeful act may be to sit still. The individual who succeeds in realizing and expressing the truth which is in him may be said to have performed an act more potent than the destruction of an empire. It is not always necessary, moreover, to mouth the truth. Though the world crumble and dissolve truth abides.

In the beginning was the Word. Man acts it out. He is the act, not the actor.

One *can* live joyously – one must! – in the midst of a world peopled with sorrowing, suffering creatures. What other world is there in which to enjoy life? I know this, that I will no longer perform for the sake of performing, nor take action for the sake of being active. Nor can I acknowledge as necessitous or inevitable what now goes on in the name of law and order, peace and prosperity, freedom and security. Sell it to the Hottentots! It's too utterly horrendous for me to swallow. I intend to stake out my own claim, a tiny one, but my own. Lacking a name for it, I'll call it – *pro tem* – The Land of Fuck.

I have already made mention of this bizarre domain. I spoke of it as an 'Interlude'. I mention it again because more than ever now it has the ring of reality. In this domain I am the undisputed monarch. Mad as a hatter, perhaps, but only because 999,999,999,999 others think other than I do. Where others see celery roots, kohlrabi, parsnips and rootabaga, I detect a new sprout – the germ of a new order.

What man's sex life may be under a new order

surpasses my feeble imagination to describe. We know something of the frenzy and ecstasy which characterize the rites and ceremonies of pagans and primitives; we know something too of the art and the delicacy which govern the act of love among oriental devotees. But we have never seen or heard of a people free from superstition, ritual, idolatry, fear or guilt. Some have been free in some respects, others in other respects. Not even in Arthur's time, and it was a glorious one, did man show himself free.

It is our dream life which offers a key to the possibilities in store for us. In dream it is the Adamic man, one with the earth, one with the stars, who comes to life, who roams through past, present and future with equal freedom. For him there are no taboos, no laws, no conventions. Pursuing his way, he is unimpeded by time, space, physical obstacles or moral considerations. He sleeps with his mother as naturally as with another. If it be with an animal of the field he satisfies his desire, he feels no revolt. He can take his own daughter with equal enjoyment and satisfaction.

In the waking world, shackled, crippled, paralyzed by every kind of fear, threatened at every step by real or imaginary punishments, almost every desire we seek to express is made to appear wrong or evil. The true self knows different; the moment one shuts one's eyes all these prohibited urges are indulged in riotously. In dream, despite all the barbed wire, the precipices, the traps, the monsters who lie in wait for us, we follow through. When our desires are thwarted or suppressed, life becomes mean, ugly, vicious and death-like. *Just as it is,* in other words. After all, the world we inhabit is only the reflected image of our inner chaos. Our medicine men, our juristic fanatics, all the hair-shirted pedagogues and mystifiers who dominate the scene would have us believe that to partake of a societal life, the savage, primitive being, as they call the natural man, must be hobbled and fettered. Every creative being knows that this is false. Nothing was ever accomplished by cramping, thwarting, fettering, shackling one another. Nor crime nor war, nor lust nor greed, nor malice nor envy are thus eliminated. All that is effected, in the name of society, is the perpetuation of the great lie.

To suppose that, unless restrained by fear of punishment, men will set about killing and plundering, buggering and torturing ad infinitum, is to slander the human race. Given only half a chance, men will express the best that is in them. Certainly outbursts of violence are bound to occur whenever there is a new lease of freedom. Some kind of crude justice is bound to assert itself whenever the scales have been tipped too far. Like it or not, there come times when some specimens of the race ask to be wiped out, and are wiped out, if only out of kindness, decency and reverence for those to come. There are times when some wretches deserve nothing better than to be thrown to the wolves. Now and then the real traitors to the race *must* be stripped of their unholy rights and privileges, their foul, unlawful possessions, and be driven out like dogs.

These vengeful deeds will be repeated over and over, as long as there is suppression and oppression. Do not mistake me, it is not the great in spirit who advocate such doings! But the hapless ones also have their say now and then. No one is too small or mean to be ignored, if ever a sane balance is to be achieved.

The spirit of man is like a river which seeks the sea. Damn it and you raise its force. Do not hold man responsible for his terrifying outbursts! Condemn the life force! The spirit which moves us can assume any guise: it can liken us to angels, demons or gods. To each his choice. Nothing stands in man's way but his own ghostly fears. The world is our home, but we have yet to occupy it; the woman we love awaits us, but we know not where to find her; the path we seek is under our feet, but we fail to recognize it. Whether we are of the earth for long or for short, the powers to be drawn on are unlimited.

Do we profit by our stay *ici-bas*?* How marvellous if

we could say, like the Buddha: 'I obtained not the least thing from complete, unexcelled awakening, and for this very reason it is called "complete, unexcelled awakening".'

I can imagine a world – because it has always existed! – in which man and beast choose to live in peace and harmony, a world transformed each day through the magic of love, a world free of death. It is not a dream.

The dinosaur had his day and is gone for ever. The caveman had his day and is no more. The ancestors of the present race still linger on, despised, neglected, but not yet buried. They are all reminders – of things that were and of things to come. They too had their dreams, dreams from which they never awakened.

There has never been a dream of life too splendid, too dazzling, to fit the picture of reality. Those who fear are doomed; those who doubt are lost. The Eden of the past is the utopia of the future. Between stretches the endless present, the now, in which things are the way they are, and just because it is thus and not otherwise we have all we desire, all we need, like the fish in the ocean . . . for it is an ocean we are swimming in, a vast and mighty deep, which embraces all we can ever know, ever realize . . . and is that not enough?

It's when I'm alone, walking the streets, that I get the

feel of things: past, present, future, birth, rebirth, evolution, revolution, dissolution. And sex in all its pathological pathos.

Each country, each city, town and village has its own sexual climate and atmosphere. In some places it permeates the air like thin, vaporous sperm; in others it is caked into the walls of dwellings, even houses of worship. Here, like a carpet of fresh new grass, it gives off a sweet, tonic perfume; there, thick as fluff and swept about like pollen, it sticks to one's garments, gets in one's hair, stops the ears. Sometimes the lack of it is so striking that to catch just a whiff of it is electrifying. (Like coming upon a show window in a dark street and finding twenty-three white chicks wide awake under the merciless glare of a row of naked bulbs.)

The way people talk, the way they walk, the way they dress, the way they eat and where, the way they look at one another, every detail, every gesture they make reveals the presence or the absence of sex. And then there are the murderers of sex – one recognizes them instantly anywhere.

Now and then, in my strolls, I happen along just as a manikin is singled out for attention. There she stands nude as wax, exposed to full view. The window-dresser has just put his arms around her to move her this way or that. Amazing how alive the manikin seems! Not only alive, but slightly lascivious. As for the window-trimmer, everything about him suggests the mortician.

Roaming about at night, it always seems to me that the dismal quarters of a town are more alive, more intriguing, than the brilliantly lit boulevards, where the manikins, real and artificial, are dressed to kill. Take Grasse, for example. It can be terrifying and seductive after dark. Against the base of the hill, where the poor are gathered like maggots, the streets seem to be laid out like curling papers. At every turn there are heaps of refuse surrounded by mangy-looking cats eating their fill. In summer the doorways are draped with toothless hags who sit and gossip by the murky light of a street lamp. Above the cackle of the crones there can be heard now and then the coarse laugh of a whore. The effect is theatrical. To spot a slovenly bitch sprawled over a doorstep, her thighs exposed, her limbs wide apart, is an inflammatory sight which the filth and squalor of the surroundings only serve to accentuate. One wanders about in a daze, returning again and again to the heavy figure with legs spread open like a compass and in the sockets of the eyes two huge black coals burning.

Whenever there is a river, a marketplace, a cathedral, a railway station, a gambling casino, there smoulders this swamp-fire which thickens the blood and makes the mouth dry.

It is a natural thing to gravitate towards the bright lights when one comes upon a strange city after dark. My instinct is to move towards the dark places, where the silence is punctuated by ribald shouts, coarse laughter, filthy oaths and meaningless grunts . . . or now and then a sob. The sound of someone sobbing behind a shuttered window reduces me to ashes. I am not only moved to the depths, I am often sexually excited. A woman sobbing in the dark so often means a woman begging for love. I tell myself that her sobs will soon be stifled by a passionate embrace; I wait to hear the squeals and grunts which follow.

Moving from house to house, window to window, my forlorn hope is to catch sight of a woman bidding herself goodnight in a cracked mirror. If only once I could catch that last look before the light is blown out!

Over all the land are places set apart, where men and women twitch and toss on beds of stone, their fevered brows trickling with sweat, their addled brains teeming with futile hopes and vengeful dreams . . . Again I see that little town in the Peloponnese with its dungeon overlooking the harbour; all is buried deep in sleep except this hideous place, a cage of stone and iron which blazes with a ghastly light, as if the very souls of the condemned had been set afire. At the foot of the walls, where all the twisted lanes came to an end, I saw a couple locked in everlasting embrace. Nearby, blissfully nibbling the brush, a billy goat was anchored. I watched them awhile, the goat and the oblivious lovers, then sauntered down to the quay where a daffy old salt with a white beard sat bathing his feet. His gaze, riveted on distant Argos, was that of a man hoping to catch sight of the golden fleece.

In their loneliness, in their dream of love or lack of it, the lost are ever drifting to the water's edge. In the immense drift of night the whistling agony of the tormented is muffled by the lap-lap of even the tiniest stream. The mind, emptied of all but the lapping of waves, grows tranquil. Rolling with the waters, the spirit that was harried folds its wings.

The waters of the earth! Levelling, sustaining, comforting. Baptismal waters! Next to light, the most mysterious element of creation.

Everything passes away in time. The waters abide.

February–April, 1957
Big Sur, California

Notes

p. 1, 1940. MILLER'S NOTE.

p. 7, Published first in *Max and the White Phagocytes*, Obelisk Press, Paris, 1938. MILLER'S NOTE.

p. 9, See reference to this and other 'gratuitous' passages in *Big Sur and the Oranges of Hieronymus Bosch.* (New Directions, N. Y., 1957.) MILLER'S NOTE.

p. 17, 'Story' (French).

p. 54, 'However' (French).

p. 59, *'Dieu est le grand solitaire qui ne parle qu'aux solitaires et qui ne fait participer à sa puissance, à sa sagesse, à sa félicité, que ceux qui participent, en quelque manière, à son éternelle solitude.'* (Léon Bloy) ['God is the great recluse who only speaks to recluses and lets only those partake in his power, his wisdom, his happiness, who in some way or another partake in his eternal solitude.'] MILLER'S NOTE.

p. 67, 'Landlady' (French).

p. 73, *Caliban Parle,* by Jean Guéhenno: Editions Grasset, Paris. MILLER'S NOTE. The quotation translates: 'The true treason is to follow the way of the crowd, and to use the intellect to justify it.'

p. 78, 'Here below' (French).

Miller's Corrections to the Original Text

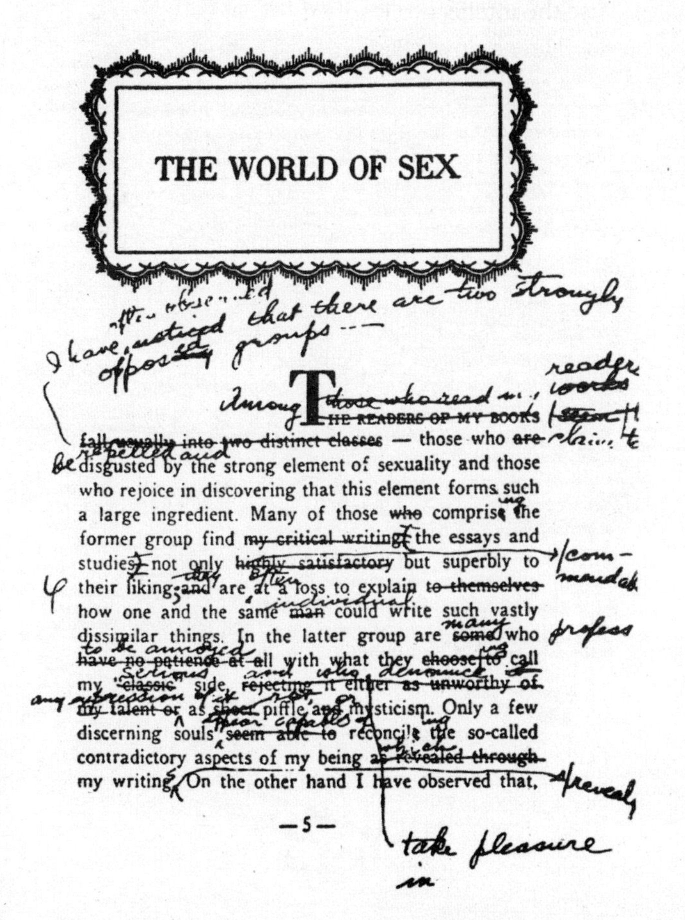

THE WORLD OF SEX

THE READERS OF MY BOOKS fall usually into two distinct classes — those who are disgusted by the strong element of sexuality and those who rejoice in discovering that this element forms such a large ingredient. Many of those who comprise the former group find my critical writings—the essays and studies—not only highly satisfactory but superbly to their liking, and are at a loss to explain to themselves how one and the same man could write such vastly dissimilar things. In the latter group are some who have no patience at all with what they choose to call my "classic" side, rejecting it either as unworthy of my talent or as sheer piffle and mysticism. Only a few discerning souls seem able to reconcile the so-called contradictory aspects of my being as revealed through my writing. On the other hand I have observed that,

—5—

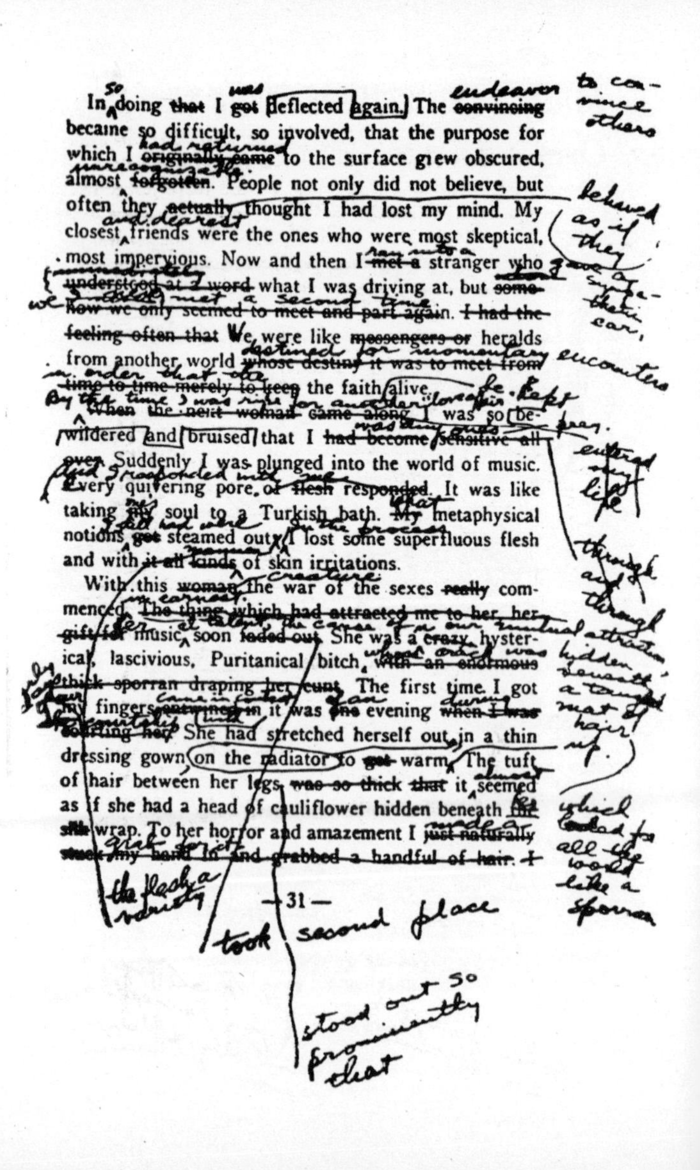
In doing that I got deflected again. The convincing became so difficult, so involved, that the purpose for which I originally came to the surface grew obscured, almost forgotten. People not only did not believe, but often they actually thought I had lost my mind. My closest friends were the ones who were most skeptical, most impervious. Now and then I met a stranger who understood at a word what I was driving at, but somehow we only seemed to meet and part again. I had the feeling often that we were like messengers or heralds from another world whose destiny it was to meet from time to time merely to keep the faith alive.

When the next woman came along I was so bewildered and bruised that I had become sensitive all over. Suddenly I was plunged into the world of music. Every quivering pore of flesh responded. It was like taking my soul to a Turkish bath. My metaphysical notions got steamed out; I lost some superfluous flesh and with it all kinds of skin irritations.

With this woman the war of the sexes really commenced. The thing which had attracted me to her, her gift for music, soon faded out. She was a crazy, hysterical, lascivious, Puritanical bitch, with an enormous thick sporran draping her cunt. The first time I got my fingers entwined in it was one evening when I was courting her. She had stretched herself out in a thin dressing gown on the radiator to get warm. The tuft of hair between her legs was so thick that it seemed as if she had a head of cauliflower hidden beneath the silk wrap. To her horror and amazement I just naturally stuck my hand in and grabbed a handful of hair. I beautiful emotional death, perhaps, but death. I wanted to go forward, forward at all costs. She must have known that I was standing there wavering; she must have exerted all her will to hold me in that wild outburst of grief. But it failed. I stood there just a few moments, absolutely paralyzed, and then suddenly I bolted. In the street I actually began to run, as though in fear that she might come after me and pull me back with tear-stained hands. And as I ran the tears were streaming from my eyes, the dry brutal sobs choked me. I walked and walked to calm myself down and to make myself presentable to the woman who was waiting for me. Nearing the house I began to weep again. I was weeping for joy that I had found some one whom I truly loved, some one with whom I could make a new and deeper life. The woman lying on the floor had receded into the past. It was as though it had all happened years ago, in some other life. I was thinking only of the one who was waiting for me, of the joy we would experience together. I was on the point of buying some flowers for her, but checked the impulse because of the fear that she might interpret it strangely. It was difficult for her, these weekly excursions. She never said anything about it, but I could see from the look in her eye when I set out each time that it was painful. Usually she had things to do when I went off by myself, but on these days she never knew what to do with herself, she was confused, bewildered, irritated in spite of herself. And always, as I was leaving, I would say that I would be back soon, and of course I always returned late. As I walked up the stoop I was

It would be a

Paralyzed for a few moments, suddenly came to — and I bolted.

fearful, I suppose, that she would

when I went to see the child

she knew how to busy herself in my absence,

them. I mean that we would drop our tools, quit our jobs, deny our obligations, pay no taxes, observe no laws, and so on. Could the man or woman who is thoroughly awakened possibly do the crazy things which are now expected of him and her every moment of the day? Every class of society is restless, miserable, unhappy, unsatisfied. The rich are not a whit better off than the poor, though outwardly they may seem to be. Our mode of life makes us all enchained, all victims, whether we be on top, below, or in the middle. No one is immune. "One must live quite apart, forgetting," said Lawrence somewhere. He tried it and failed. One cannot live apart. Whatever is ugly or evil in the external pattern is thus and so only because of the inner pattern and this inner pattern is a mode or condition of life which permeates everywhere. I am speaking now only of our Western way of living, of this modern world which is expropriating the older worlds. There are still places in the world where a totally different way of life prevails, but they are not for us. Despite all the newfangled ways and means of communicating we remain impervious to their mode of life. Peoples, like individuals, have their own unique destinies. We hear and learn about the manners and customs of remote peoples, but we are powerless to alter our lives in the light of this knowledge. We have a rhythm and a pattern which is ours, and even the knowledge that there may be other, better ways of living does not affect our behavior. Now and then an individual breaks loose and adopts another mode of life. But he is only the exception which proves the rule. The great personality is he who

Throughout all history only a handful of men ever broke the mould. And though they established a way of life which was their own, those who imitated them have failed. Clear as their message was, even the greatest spirits have misunderstood. To follow, not to lead, that is man's curse.